More Classic Irish Myths, Legends, and Heroes

Stories adapted by Ann Carroll
and illustrated by Derry Dillon

IRELAND'S BEST KNOWN STORIES
IN A NUTSHELL

Published 2016
by: In a Nutshell
an imprint of Poolbeg Press Ltd

123 Grange Hill, Baldoyle
Dublin 13, Ireland

Text © Poolbeg Press Ltd 2016

1

A catalogue record for this book is available from the British Library.

ISBN 978 1 78199-899-1

Cover design and illustrations by Derry Dillon
Printed and bound by CPI Group (UK) Ltd, Croydon, CR0 4YY

This book belongs to

- -

CONTENTS

Granuaile
The Pirate Queen

In the year 1544, when Grace O'Malley was about fourteen, girls from wealthy families were expected to be good at needlework and dancing, to have charming manners, to please with their singing and to look beautiful.

Grace's mother, Margaret, pointed this out. Often.

Her daughter's reply was always the same: "I'm not interested in any of that!"

Her mother sighed. "You'll never get a husband at this rate."

"I don't like husbands. They always want their wives to stay at home."

Her mother sighed again, thinking how difficult Grace was and how she didn't seem to like anything she was supposed to like.

"So what do you want to do with your life?"
she asked rather impatiently one day.

"Well, what I want – what I'd really, really
like – is to be a sailor and go with Father to
Spain on his next voyage."

Margaret felt faint. "It's your father I blame," she said. "Eoghan should never have let you near a boat!" And she sent a servant to fetch him.

Eoghan O'Malley was Chief of his clan. A great seafarer and trader, he was a rich man and the family lived in a castle on Clew Bay in Mayo. He loved his daughter and from the time she was small had taken her on short trips around the bay. But he never thought she'd want to sail the ocean.

Now he told her, using the Gaelic form of her name, "Gráinne, that's out of the question. Only men and boys are sailors. Girls are not." His daughter's face was stubborn. How could he make her see sense? Then he remembered how proud she was of her beautiful long hair.

"You can't do it. For one thing your hair would get caught in the ropes of the ship."

Later in her room, Grace sat at the mirror and muttered, "If long hair doesn't suit, then I don't like long hair!" and she cut it all off.

Her mother wept. Her father laughed, but stuffed a handkerchief in his mouth when he saw his wife's face.

"I can't bear to look at you!" said Margaret. "Your beautiful hair! You look like a hedgehog!"

"Now Father has no excuse for not taking me with him," Grace said.

Eoghan scratched his head. Margaret cried. Grace looked determined.

"Well," Eoghan said at last, "it might be a good thing all round." He gazed at his sobbing wife. "Margaret, you won't have to look at that bald head." He turned to his daughter. "And you, Gráinne Mhaol – Baldheaded Grace – will soon learn that a sailor's life is not for a lady!"

And that is how Grace O'Malley became a seafarer and got the nickname 'Granuaile', short for Gráinne Mhaol.

Grace loved the great sailing ships and the long voyages and earned the respect of the rough sailors. She was afraid of nothing and worked as hard as any. Yet she had a soft side and if one of the crew got sick she was very caring. In a short time the men would do anything for her and thought it an excellent thing to have a girl on board.

As she grew older Grace took charge when her father had business at home. Any fishing boat or ship that sailed around Clew Bay had to pay a tax to the O'Malleys. Sometimes a new captain thought it unmanly to hand over gold coins to a girl. If he was foolish enough to say so, he'd be forced to pay double. In time she became known as the Pirate Queen.

Margaret needn't have worried that her daughter would never marry. When she was eighteen, Grace met Dónal O'Flaherty. He was a fine, handsome man who was in line to rule all of West Connacht one day.

I like him, Grace thought. I really, really like him, for he loves an adventure and a good fight.

I'll have no peace with her, Dónal thought, for she's not one to sit by the fire. But that suits me and I'll ask her to be my wife.

"Yes!" she said at once. "As long as you don't expect me to stay at home."

"I don't. But I do expect you to move to my castle at Bunowen in Connemara."

And so they married, moved to Bunowen and had three children: Eoghan, Margaret and Murrough. The years passed and the children grew up. Then Dónal took on one fight too many and was killed in battle. Grace was heartbroken and moved the family back to Clew Bay.

By this stage many men saw her as a great
leader and followed her to Mayo.

Some time later she married Richard Bourke – known as Iron Richard because of his coat of mail – and they had one son, Tibbot. But after a year Grace grew tired of her new husband.

I don't like him, she thought. He could never compare to Dónal. A coat of mail doesn't make him a great man!

So she locked herself in Bourke's home, Rockfleet Castle, while he was away, and worked out a plan.

From a high window she watched for his return and when he rode into the yard she called down to him three times: "Richard Bourke, I dismiss you!" Under Brehon Law this was divorce and she could keep the castle since she was in it.

At this time Ireland was ruled by England. The Irish often ignored English laws and those in the West ignored them the most, following the old Brehon Law, particularly when it suited.

"Those people in the West of Ireland are out of control!" Queen Elizabeth the First of England said. "Especially Grace O'Malley. And I don't like it! Something will have to be done!"

Then she decided, "I will make Richard Bingham Governor of Connacht. He is a tough, nasty man and will do the job well."

"You must restore order," she told Bingham. "I want that woman, Grace O'Malley, to show some respect. She breaks our laws, attacks our ships and robs their treasure. They call her the Pirate Queen. I don't like that for there is only one queen and that's me!"

"Indeed, Your Majesty, I will teach her a lesson. She must learn that you are the true Pirate Queen!"

Her Majesty was most indignant. "I'm no pirate!" she said.

Well, all your sea captains have orders to raid any foreign ship they come across, Bingham thought, but didn't say. The Queen's face was very frosty and he didn't want his head chopped off.

His revenge on Grace was cruel for he arranged the murder of Eoghan, her eldest son. Then he stole her cattle and land and as a final blow, kidnapped her other two sons. But he could not break her spirit.

"I will not beg that creature to free my sons," she vowed. "Instead I will speak to Elizabeth as one woman to another."

And so she set sail for England.

But before she was allowed to see Elizabeth she had to answer eighteen questions about her life and family, about Brehon Law and about how much power women had in Ireland.

Grace did not speak English and no one at the palace knew Gaelic, so the questions were in Latin, the language of Europe's courts, which Grace had learned as a child.

"Good Lord," Elizabeth said when she read the document, "I like these answers for this woman has led a most interesting life. I must see her."

It is said the two got on very well, talking away in Latin.

Then Elizabeth said, "If you promise to stop raiding ships and breaking English laws, I will order Bingham to return to England after he has freed your sons and given back your cattle and land."

Grace promised, but things didn't quite work out. She got her sons back, but nothing else. And Bingham stayed only a short time in England before returning to Connacht. So Grace went back to her old ways, but Bingham never got the better of her again.

Always Grace loved the sea and when life was quiet she would explore the Irish coast. Once, it is said, she stopped at Howth in Dublin and decided to call in at Howth Castle, home of the St Lawrences. But when the owners saw her and her large crew arriving they shut the gates against her.

"I want to have my dinner in peace," St Lawrence said, "and not with a lot of uninvited sailors!"

"No food!" Grace was raging. "I don't like it! They're so mean and we're so starving."

So Grace kidnapped his ten-year-old son. To get him back, St Lawrence had to promise never to do the like again. In fact, he promised always to have an extra place set at the table just in case someone arrived unexpectedly.

The Pirate Queen became very rich. By the end of her life she owned herds of cattle and horses and quite a few castles as well as gold and silver.

Grace died in 1603, having lived the way she wanted at a time when most girls and women had no say at all in their own lives.

Now, in Westport House in Mayo, built on the site of one of Grace's castles, her life is celebrated in an exhibition to The Pirate Queen, and in the grounds there is an exciting Pirate Adventure Park.

And sometimes, they say, a whisper can be heard in those great halls: "What I'd like . . . what I'd really, really like . . . is to go with Father to Spain on his next voyage . . ."

The End

Word Sounds

(Opinions may differ regarding pronunciation)

Words	Sounds
Eoin	Owen
Grainne	Grawn-yeh
Grainne Mhaol	Grawn-yeh Wail
Granuaile	Same as above
Murrough	Murr-eh
Brehon	Bre-hon

Oisín and Tír na nÓg

Long, long ago in Ireland, when this story began, Oisín spent the day on the seashore with the Fianna, a band of warriors led by his father, Fionn Mac Cumhaill. They were famous for their strength and bravery, and none more so than Oisín. On this day, testing his skills against the rest, he was the fastest on horseback, strongest at wrestling, best with spear and javelin. And by sunset he was still full of energy.

How wonderful it is to be young, he thought. How sad that youth can't last forever!

His father was looking tired and old. Fionn was once the greatest warrior of all; now he was heading for home and sleep.

Turning his horse, Oisín caught up on Fionn
and the rest followed. He shouted to his dogs,
"Bran, Sceolain! Home!" Together the warriors
galloped along the shore.

"Look! Oisín, look! On the waves!" one of the warriors called.

From far out on the red-gold sea came a girl on horseback. Amazed, they stopped.

"She's beautiful," Oisín said, enchanted by her golden hair and bright blue eyes.

"She'll bring no luck," Fionn said. As a boy he had tasted the Salmon of Knowledge and could see into the future. "Let's go now!"

But Oisín was watching the girl gallop closer. His father sighed. So much heartache lay ahead.

It's good to be old, he thought. At least I won't live to see his sorrows.

"Oisín!" the girl called, stopping her white horse before him. "I am Niamh Chinn Óir and I've come from Tír na nÓg to take you back with me." Niamh Chinn Óir meant 'Niamh of the Golden Hair'.

His friends gasped. Tír na nÓg was a magical place beyond the seas where no one ever grew old. They envied Oisín. But Fionn's heart sank.

"In the Land of Youth you'll always be as strong and handsome as you are today," Niamh continued. "There will be music and feasting, stories and contests, the best of horses and hounds, great castles to live in, as much gold and silver as you could wish for."

"And you?" Oisín asked. "Will you be with me?"

Niamh smiled. "We'll be young together for always."

And so, in spite of his father's sadness, Oisín left with Niamh on her great white horse and they galloped back across the sea.

It was just as Niamh promised. In Tír na nÓg it was always perfect summer. Everyone was young. There was no sickness or death. He loved Niamh and she loved him. She was beautiful beyond compare.

And yet . . . and yet . . .

Before long he found he missed home. He missed the seasons, the countryside, his friends. He missed his dogs, Bran and Sceolan, and the chat around the camp fire. Most of all he missed his father. If only we could talk once again, he thought.

But Niamh didn't want him to leave. "I can't go with you for I can't live where humans live. But I'll take you to the Island of Music and Merriment. There you'll be happy again."

And because he loved her, Oisín agreed to go. The music on this island cheered his heart and he was merry, until the day Niamh asked him to sing. His song was about the Fianna and the battles they'd fought. It was about bravery and friendship and it made him sad.

"I must go back," he told Niamh. "I must see them once again."

"We'll go to the Island of Victories," Niamh told him. "And there you can fight to your heart's content. It's the battles you miss, Oisín, not the warriors."

And because he didn't wish to leave her, Oisín agreed.

He fought many battles on that island, alongside great warriors. But although the fights were fierce, once Oisín realised he couldn't lose, they were meaningless. All the old sorrows returned.

"There's no point to this," he told Niamh. "No point at all. I can't forget home, or the Fianna or my father. I must go back."

"You're just weary," Niamh said, "and you will forget if we go to the Island of Sleep."

And again, Oisín agreed.

On the Island of Sleep they found a sheltered cove with white sand where the breeze brushed the waves, and Oisín fell into a slumber. But sleep brought no forgetfulness. Dreams of the Fianna crowded his mind. In one he heard his father ask, "Which of these islands, Oisín, is the Island of Happiness?"

Then he awoke, his heart full of misery. Niamh could not bear his sadness and told him, "Go! But if you do, you may not be able to come back."

"I will come back!" Oisín vowed. "All I want is to see my old friends again, to watch Bran and Sceolain race through the woods, to talk with Fionn once more and to see the land where I grew up. Less than a day, Niamh, will satisfy me. After that I'll return."

Niamh said, "Then you must let my horse carry you and you must promise not to set foot on the ground of your homeland. If you do, you'll never come back!"

Oisín promised and, because she loved him, Niamh let him go. As she watched him gallop across the waves she thought: What good is eternal youth if it brings eternal sorrow?

It seemed to Oisín only a few years had passed since he'd left home and that he'd spent only a short time on each magical island. He expected everything at home to be the same, and at first when he rode ashore he thought it was. The mountains hadn't changed, nor had the long shoreline. But as he galloped inland he saw

small stone buildings he didn't recognise. They had crosses on them. When he heard a bell peal from one of the buildings he stopped and watched, stunned, as people flocked towards it.

What had happened to everyone? They were so small! A curse must have fallen on them. They too stopped to stare at him and he galloped away.

But soon he saw other groups and noted that no man was as tall or strong as any in the Fianna. Where were his comrades? He could not find them in the old places. Indeed, the woods and fields where they'd hunted and camped were gone, villages and farmland in their place.

Then he came across six men at the edge of a meadow. They were trying to lift a huge rock and he stopped to ask if they knew where the Fianna were.

"The Fianna?" One of the men stepped towards him. "They're long gone!"

"I can see that!" Oisín was impatient. "Just tell me where they've gone and I'll be on my way."

"To their graves," the man said. "The last of the Fianna died three hundred years ago."

For a while Oisín couldn't speak with sorrow and his mind struggled to understand. Time mustn't exist in Tír na nÓg, he thought. How could I

believe only a short time had passed there? I've
been away at least three centuries!

Silently he brooded and the man went back
to helping the others lift the rock. But the rock
wouldn't budge.

This is a different world! Oisín thought. I must get back to Niamh. There's nothing here for me.

But first he would help the men – a simple task.

"Where do you want to put that stone?"

"Stone?" They looked at each other before answering. "At the edge of the sea," they said. "But it's impossible to move!"

Oisin leaned down from the horse, lifted the huge rock with one hand and flung it far away to the edge of the sea. But the saddle had slipped around with him, the straps broke and he tumbled to the ground.

The great horse turned at once and galloped away.

Mouths open, the men watched as the handsome young warrior changed instantly. His hair turned grey and wispy and a thousand wrinkles creased his face. They could see the bones beneath his skin and stepped back, horrified.

Oisín tried to stand and as they watched his efforts the men felt great pity.

"He is so old," one said.

"He needs help. We'll take him to Patrick."

Patrick was the man who'd brought Christianity to Ireland. The men gently carried Oisín to his church, where he was made comfortable.

Over the next few days Patrick listened to his story. In turn he told him about God and Heaven.

Oisín was curious. "If I become a Christian will I go to this Heaven?" he asked.

"You will."

"What's Heaven like?"

"A place where there is no more sickness and no more death and it's always summer."

"And will my dogs, Bran and Sceolain, be there?"

"Certainly not. Dogs have no souls."

"What about Fionn? And the Fianna? Will they be there."

"They were pagans, not Christians. No, they won't be there!"

Oisín thought for a while then said, "Heaven sounds just like Tír na nÓg. It's not for me. When the Fianna die, they go to the House of the Fianna in the Otherworld. That's where I'll go. My dogs will be glad to see me. Fionn and my friends will be there, impatient to tell me all that's happened. Maybe I'll see Niamh too, for I think she could live in such a place."

Patrick saw there was no changing his mind and spoke no more of Heaven.

So Oisín spent the short time that remained to him dreaming of the House of the Fianna where all those he loved would be waiting for him.

The End

Word Sounds

(Opinions may differ regarding pronunciation)

Words	*Sounds*
Oisín	Usheen
Tír na nÓg	Teer na nogue (nogue rhymes with rogue)
Fianna	Fee-anna
Fionn	Fee-un
Mac	Mock
Cumhaill	Cool
Sceolain	Skeo-lan
Niamh	Neeve

The Story of Brian Boru

One: A Fighting Family

When Brian Boru was born around the year 940, there were 150 kings in Ireland and one High King. This was an awful lot of rulers for such a small country. And they were always fighting, always trying to get more land, more power, more wealth.

Also there were many Vikings living here, in places like Limerick and Dublin where they'd seized power from the Irish. They too loved fighting.

So the world Brian was born into was anything but peaceful.

His father, Cennedig, was King of North Munster. Then as now Ireland was divided into four provinces: Munster, Ulster, Leinster and Connacht. Cennedig trained his sons, Mahon and Brian, to be great warriors. They could use sword, shield, sling and spear like no others, and became skilled horsemen and charioteers, able to take on the enemy with speed and accuracy, so that they were greatly feared and respected.

When Cennedig died, Mahon, the eldest, became king and it wasn't long before he wished to test his ability.

"What do you say, brother," he asked Brian one day, "to making our small kingdom richer?"

Brian sat up immediately. "What have you in mind?"

"I thought we might take over the Rock of Cashel. That great stronghold would bring us much in the way of wealth and power."

"What about Mael Muad, King of South Munster? He won't like the idea of you being more mighty than him!"

"He'll be happy if we help him rid Limerick of Ivar the Viking. He can't stand that Norseman. I have it all planned. What do you say, Brian?"

"Let the battle begin, brother!"

After much fighting they seized The Rock
of Cashel. Mael Muad was delighted to help,
for they drove Ivar out of Limerick and he
saw that as a great favour altogether. But then
the people were so impressed with Mahon
that they made him King of all Munster and
this didn't please Mael Muad at all.

"That fellow has rightly tricked me!" he seethed. "He had me fighting for him and now he takes my kingdom! Well, it just won't do."

Two: The Price of Power

So Mael Muad, who was a sneaky character, plotted and watched and waited. When the time was right – when Brian was off on other business – he swooped on Cashel, seized power and killed Mahon.

Meanwhile Ivar the Viking took advantage of all the brouhaha and kerfuffle to slip back into Limerick.

Brian was dismayed. "My brother killed and Ivar back in town. It won't do!"

First he marched on Limerick and in the fierce battle that followed Ivar was killed. Then Brian turned his sights on Cashel and challenged Mael Muad to one-to-one combat. The man did his best but was outclassed. Brian killed him quickly and impressed friend and foe with his strength and skill.

Now he was King of all Munster.

He proved a great leader and allowed
many of the Vikings to stay in Limerick.
They promised loyalty and the use of their
fine ships. This delighted him, for the ships
were very well made.

Three: Ambition

Brian was extremely ambitious. "Why should I be satisfied with Munster only?" he reasoned. "What about Leinster? I'd be a better ruler there any day than Mael Sechnall, our wonderful High King!"

And so his army and navy travelled towards Leinster. Again and again he attacked the forces of the High King, trapping them between sea and land. He planned well and he was brave and his men trusted him.

The High King saw he could not win and in 996 he handed over Leinster to Brian.

But a chieftain called Mael Morda was raging at this outcome. He had his own army and had taken the High King's side, hoping to be well rewarded for his troubles. Instead he got nothing. He turned on the High King and in no time at all took away the rest of his kingdom, except for Meath.

Brian wasn't a bit pleased at this interference! It's not at all easy being powerful, he thought. I sort out one rival and another comes along in his place. It won't do at all – just as well I like a good fight.

Mael Morda knew he'd made a powerful enemy and moved his army to Dublin looking for help from his nephew by marriage, the powerful Viking, Sitric Silkbeard, who ruled the city.

Good! Brian thought. Two foes with one slingshot! I will lay siege to Dublin and get rid of them both.

But the enemy moved their forces out of the city before Brian could block them.

"We'll fight at Glen Mama," Sitric said to Mael Morda. "There we can meet Brian and his army face to face without fear of traps, for the valley is wide and open, so there'll be no sneaking up on us."

The battle at Glen Mama was ferocious. It is said 4000 warriors from both sides died before Brian eventually won.

Mael Morda tried to hide in a tree but was pulled down by Brian's son and taken prisoner.

Four: Brian's Genius

Brian knew his men were feeling low and so
he told them: "Victory is ours. Most of Mael
Morda's men are dead. So even though we've
lost many friends, this is a great result. You
fought bravely and now you deserve a fine
reward. We'll march on Dublin and each of
you may seize what you want from the city!"

His men cheered and said there never was a better leader. And so they sacked Dublin, looting their way through the streets until Brian called a halt and the soldiers left, satisfied.

It was then Brian showed real genius. Time to make friends with the enemy, he thought. Sitric will expect me to kill him. Instead I'll leave him to rule Dublin on my behalf. And I'll release Mael Morda. No doubt he'll be grateful and do my bidding.

His daughter married Sitric and Brian himself married Sitric's mother, the widow Gormflaith, who was Irish and the sister of Mael Morda. This was Brian's fourth marriage and he already had a number of children.

Now we're all one family, he thought, pleased. And I'm the Head of everyone.

Then the people of Connacht made him their king, wanting his protection, and by the year 1002, Brian was accepted as High King of Ireland by all except the people of Ulster.

Five: War against Ulster

"He's nothing but an upstart!" the Ulstermen said. "A petty ruler from North Munster. He has no right to be High King!"

But Brian was determined.

It's better for a country to have one proper leader, he thought, than many who are always battling. I'll fight and I'll win against Ulster. Then there'll be peace.

But the war lasted ten years. One of Ulster's allies was Mael Morda, who'd been released after the Battle of Glen Mama. He hated Brian's guts. The other was Sitric, who in 1012 grew tired of being the High King's lackey.

Brian marched on Dublin. Inside the city were Sitric, Mael Morda and their Ulster allies. This time the enemy was too strong for Brian and managed to keep him outside the walls. Soon his forces were short of food.

If we stay we'll starve, he thought. Worse, we'll lose and that won't do! And so he ordered a retreat.

The Ulstermen took this as a victory and went home.

Mael Morda knew better. "Brian will want to finish us off," he told Sitric. "But it will take him a long time to organise a proper attack. Meanwhile, if you go to Orkney and the Isle of Man, it's likely the Vikings there will help us. They love a good fight. Tell them their reward will be land and riches."

Six: The Last Battle

So on Palm Sunday, 1014, Sigurd of Orkney and Brodir from the Isle of Man landed with a great army in Dublin. Mael Morda and Sitric joined them at Clontarf on the north coast of Dublin. Brian marched to meet them and on Good Friday the brutal battle began.

It lasted all day. The clang of shield and sword could be heard across the bay. Mael Morda was one of the first killed but soon the ground was littered with bodies and the air filled with keening for dead comrades.

Brian fought ferociously, but he was 73 years old and his men feared that he would tire and be killed. Alive, he could inspire them all. But if he died they would lose heart.

So they set up a tent for him where he could rest from time to time. But he refused, thinking he'd look weak. It was only when he knew the Vikings were being driven back that he decided to use the tent, but not for rest.

"I wish to thank God," he told his men. "I want no one guarding me when I pray. My words are for God alone."

Outside, the battle still raged. Brodir had seen his enemy slip away and sneaked after him. Silently he entered the tent. Brian was kneeling in prayer, unaware. Swiftly Brodir raised his great sword and killed the High King.

Brian's side had won, but when they found his body all his men felt the loss. They knew he'd been the best leader Ireland had ever had and there were no victory celebrations. He was buried at Armagh Cathedral and was mourned deeply.

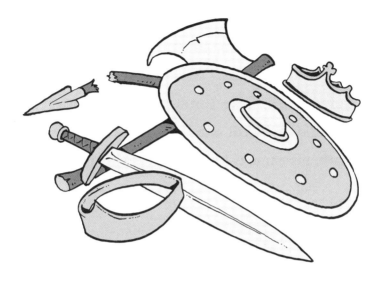

Seven: Final Word

Brian had lived in bloodthirsty times and his life was spent fighting. He'd never have lasted so long had he not been a great warrior and chieftain. Always willing to take on his enemies, he was also willing to treat them generously after battle.

He was seen as the last great High King who tried to unite the country and who drove back the Vikings. The stories of his deeds were passed down through the centuries.

Today in 2014, one thousand years after his death, his name is famous and his life is a legend.

The End

Word Sounds

(Opinions may differ regarding pronunciation)

Words	Sounds
Boru	Boroo
Cennedig	Kennedig
Maol	Mwale
Muad	Moo-ad
Mael	Male
Sechnall	Sek-nal
Morda	More-da
Sitric	Sitrick
Gormflaith	Gurm-fla
Sigurd	Sig-oord
Brodir	Bro-deer

Deirdre of the Sorrows

Long, long ago Conor Mac Nessa was King of Ulster. He was a most important man and lived in a palace at Eamhain Macha. He led an army of warriors called the Knights of the Red Branch. And he had a famous druid named Cafad who could see into the future and give Conor suitable advice – if only Conor would listen properly!

One day Cafad arrived at the palace in a great flurry of upset and told the King and his knights: "A girl-child has been born today whose beauty will bring war and death to this kingdom."

Conor's warriors immediately wanted the baby killed but Conor demanded to know more. "Who is she and how beautiful will she be?"

"She's the child of your favourite storyteller, Phelim, and is called Deirdre. She will be most attractive. Delightful! Exquisite and charming! There'll be no one like her, really. But her loveliness will bring only tragedy to Ulster!"

"I see," Conor said, pondering, while his men clamoured to have the child destroyed.

"She'll be the most beautiful girl in all of Ireland, possibly in the whole world," Cafad added gloomily.

"Then I will keep her for myself!" Conor proclaimed. "I will have her taken from her family immediately and sent away so that no man in Ulster will see her until we're married. That way there'll be no wars."

Well, the knights were very impressed. Such a wise king, they said. Such a generous heart! Imagine giving up the peace of old age to marry a gorgeous young girl . . . Weren't they lucky to have a leader who always put his kingdom first!

The more praise Conor heard, the more pleased he was.

Cafad on the other hand went home in a dudgeon, knowing the King's plan was no good but knowing there was no point in saying so, for Conor wouldn't want to hear.

So the baby was given to Lavarcham, an old woman who lived in the forest a long way from Eamhain Macha. Lavarcham loved the child and Deirdre grew up always knowing she was to marry a king and live in a palace.

Over the years Conor often asked for a
report on Deirdre's beauty and Lavarcham
could only say there never was and never
would be anyone so lovely. And she always
added: "But she's too young yet to marry."

One day Deirdre told the old woman about a dream she'd had. "I saw a young man, Lavarcham, and he was so handsome, with black hair and bright blue eyes. He was tall and a fine warrior and looked at me with love."

"That's young Naoise," Lavarcham said. "I've seen him on my visits to Eamhain Macha. No other man has such bright eyes!"

"You've seen him!" Deirdre could hardly believe it. "Then you must arrange for us to meet."

And Lavarcham at once realised how much better suited Naoise was to her young charge than the ageing king.

She thought of the unfairness of Deirdre's life: "Taken from her parents – never having other children to play with – never having any company except mine – and all because that old king says so – and now she's expected to marry him! It will not do!"

So she arranged for Deirdre and Naoise to meet in the forest.

Deirdre fell instantly in love. Naoise struggled to be sensible, though sense didn't last long, for he had never met anyone as lovely as Deirdre.

"Everyone knows you're promised to the King," he said. "And the King is my chief and I must be loyal. You and I are not meant for each other, Deirdre . . . Are we?"

"Of course we are! I never gave my promise to the King. I was never asked. It would be a forced marriage now that I've met you!"

Naoise was pleased and said, "We must leave Ireland, for Conor will have us killed if he knows we are together. First I will tell my brothers, Ardan and Ainnle. Then we'll elope to Scotland."

With Lavarcham's blessing they sailed to
Scotland, and Ardan and Ainnle went with
them. Deirdre and Naoise married and his
brothers became her brothers. This was the
family she'd never had.

Five years they spent in Scotland on the shores of Loch Etive in the Highlands, close to the Falls of Lorac. During the days they hunted and fished and at night, around the fireside, the young men told Deirdre of their adventures as Knights of the Red Branch and taught her all of the songs they knew.

But the tales and the songs made the brothers homesick. There were so many people and places for them to miss. They began to talk often of what they'd be doing right then if they were at home . . .

Deirdre missed only Lavarcham, and thought Scotland a far better place than the dark Ulster forest where she'd been reared.

Back at Eamhain Macha, Conor hadn't forgotten them for his heart was filled with fury, hatred and jealousy. Lavarcham swore she knew nothing about anything. The King trusted her for he'd always thought she'd do what he told her and didn't want to believe he could have been wrong.

He sent out his spies and eventually they tracked the four to Scotland and reported to the King.

"I will have my revenge!" he swore, seething with rage.

Then he called for Fergus Mac Roich, a great warrior and leader in the Red Branch.

Hiding his true feelings, Conor said sweetly, "I am an ageing man, Fergus, and there is nothing I'd like more before I die than to make my peace with Deirdre – also with Naoise and his brothers, for they were my most promising young champions. I want you to go to Loch Etive and bring them home to Eamhain Macha. Give them my word they will have safe passage.

Fergus took with him a band of knights, including two of his sons.

Naoise and his brothers were overjoyed to see them and at once made ready for home. Fergus gave the King's promise and added his own sworn word that the four would be safe. Deirdre saw how happy her companions were and kept her misgivings quiet.

Once the group set foot in Ireland, the King put forward the date of a feast Fergus had sworn to attend and sent a messenger to tell him so.

Fergus wasn't at all suspicious. "I must leave you," he told Naoise, "but my two sons will bring you to Eamhain Macha and you have nothing to fear."

But as the group headed into Ulster, Conor sent word that they were to go to the House of the Red Branch and not to the palace at Eamhain Macha, for he could not harm the brothers if they were guests in his own home.

At the House of the Red Branch, Naoise, Ardan and Ainnle were warmly greeted by old friends and Deirdre too was welcomed for everyone believed in the King's forgiveness.

Conor pondered his next move and sent for Lavarcham. "Go and see if Deirdre is still beautiful!" he ordered.

Lavarcham was delighted to see the girl and thought: She's happy with Naoise and looks more beautiful than ever, if that's possible.

But she distrusted Conor and told him, "I'm afraid Deirdre has lost her good looks. It must be from living in the wilds of Scotland. She's most ugly and has two large pimples on her nose. Very, very large. She's not at all attractive. Horrible really!"

This time the King didn't believe her. He felt she was overdoing it and sent a spy.

Naoise and Deirdre were playing chess near an open window when Naoise glimpsed the spy peering at his wife. Swiftly he threw one of the heavy chess pieces at the fellow. Blinded in one eye, the man nevertheless ran back to the palace and told Conor: "There is no one more beautiful than Deirdre!"

At once Conor gathered his men and attacked the Red Branch House. The brothers' old friends fought alongside them until Conor called out: "Knights! You owe your loyalty to me! You took an oath and I am your king. Your promise is sacred and must be kept!"

Most of them changed sides then and the brothers were left fighting almost on their own.

The enemy hacked their way into the house and some of them grabbed Deirdre and dragged her to the King. Ardan and Ainnle killed many before they in turn were slain.

Naoise put up a tremendous fight until he too lay dead. The brothers were buried alongside each other by a lake.

No one but Conor felt joy at the outcome and some of the knights wept for their companions, remembering happier days.

Conor married Deirdre but the marriage brought him no happiness. She couldn't stand him and the only conversation they ever had was when he asked one day: "Why do you dislike me when I treat you so well?"

"Where do I begin?" Deirdre said. "You took me from my family. You killed my young husband and his brothers. You're a vicious liar, nasty and cruel."

"When you were born," the King said, "others urged me to have you killed. I saved you!"

"For what? To spend a miserable life with you? You needn't have bothered."

Then Deirdre spoke no more. But every day she thought of Naoise until within a year she had died, heartbroken.

Jealous to the end, Conor had her buried on the opposite side of the lake to Naoise. "Not even in death shall they be together!" he swore. But in the years that followed a beautiful tree grew on Naoise's grave and another on Deirdre's. They were tall with wonderful leaves and flowers and their branches stretched across the lake until they touched and entwined.

After her death the King's warriors said that Cafad's words about Deirdre all those years ago had come true, but Lavarcham asked: "Was it Deirdre with her beauty and her loving nature who brought such sorrow to Ulster? Or was it Conor, with all his bitterness and spite?"

Misfortune when it comes is often not alone, for other sorrows visited Ulster after this. Fergus Mac Roich was furious at the King's treachery and went to Connacht, joining the court of Queen Maeve. Later he fought ferociously at her side in a famous battle known as The Cattle Raid of Cooley, which brought more destruction to Ulster and death to Cúchulainn, one of its finest heroes.

But that's another story for another day.

The End

Word Sounds

(Opinions may differ regarding pronunciation)

Words	*Sounds*
Cafad	Kafad
Phelim	Fellim
Lavarcham	Lavar-kam
Eamhain	Ow-an
Macha	Macka
Naoise	Nee-sha
Ardan	Are-dan
Ainnle	An-leh
Roich	Ro-ick
Etive	Et-iv

Heroes of the Red Branch Knights

How It All Began

One day Conor, King of Ulster, was sitting in his palace at Eamhain Macha. Having a bit of free time, he started thinking: I have a lot of gold and a fine palace, so I have lots of enemies. But if I want to be a really great king I need a proper army – not just men who'll fight and then go home, but brave warriors who will live here and defend me and what's mine to the death!

Plenty of young men wanted adventure and excitement at that time in Ulster. Conor picked the bravest for his army and they killed many of his enemies. Each of them got into the habit of bringing home the head of the man he'd killed and tying it to the branch of an oak tree outside the palace. Soon the branch was red with blood and that's how the young men came to be known as the Knights of the Red Branch.

Then Conor had another thought: My army is excellent but some of my warriors are bound to be killed and I'll need to replace them. I'll start a training camp for boys where they'll learn to be great fighters! That way there'll never be a shortage.

Then he had a further thought: My camp will also train boys from other parts of the country whose parents will pay for the privilege.

Conor was so pleased with these plans, he said to himself: "Really, I'm a very fine thinker. No wonder I'm king."

The Boys' Camp

Fergus Mac Roich was the King's right-hand man and Conor put him in charge of the Boys' Training Camp.

The youngest to join was Setanta, the king's nephew, who was seven and had great strength, speed and skill. Fergus fostered him in his own house, along with Conall Cernach of Ulster, and Ferdia of Connacht. The three boys became great friends.

They learned to use sword and shield in single combat, to throw a spear with deadly accuracy and drive a chariot at speed while wielding their weapons. They also learned to race silently through the forest and to take the enemy by surprise; and if they were faced with more than one enemy, to spot the weakest first, attack swiftly, and beat them all.

They also became hurlers and jousters and on sports days would play matches and compete in races and tournaments.

Cúchulainn and Ferdia

Soon after his arrival Setanta killed the great guard-dog of Culann the blacksmith. Seeing how upset the smith was, the boy promised, "I will take the place of your hound and guard your home until you train another dog as fierce as the one I've killed. And from now on my name will be Cúchulainn or the Hound of Culann."

Cúchulainn grew up to be Ireland's greatest hero. No one could beat him in a fair fight. He was the best warrior in the whole country – probably in the whole world.

In their early teens he and Ferdia went to the Isle of Skye in Scotland and trained with Scáthach, a powerful and famous woman warrior whose name meant 'Shadowy'. Among other skills she taught them to leap high into the air over their enemies and also how to fight underwater for a long time.

Before they left, Scáthach told them: "Ferdia, you are a great and powerful young warrior. You have proved again and again that ordinary weapons can't pierce your body, for your skin is as tough as armour. It is a powerful defence in battle to have such skin."

She turned then to Cúchulainn: "You are the bravest and the best I've ever seen. Also you have a clear head, good judgement and wisdom beyond your years. Therefore it is to you I make the gift of the Gae Bolg."

The Gae Bolg was a deadly spear against which there was no defence. It pierced both shield and armour. Once lodged in the body it opened into many spikes, causing agony and death.

Ferdia was delighted for his friend. "There's no one better than you," he told him. "You deserve such a fine weapon."

Training finished, they went home, Ferdia
to Connacht and Cúchulainn to Ulster.

Conall and his Uncle Cet

Meanwhile their friend, Conall Cernach, was killing as many Connacht men as he could, even though he was half Connacht on his mother's side. At his birth, Cafad the Druid, who could see into the future, announced: "This child will grow up to kill many Connacht men."

"Then he shall not live!" said his Connacht uncle, Cet.

Snatching him from his mother's arms, Cet placed him on the ground and stood on his neck. His mother snatched him back immediately. But from then on, Conall had a crooked neck and a hatred for his uncle and for all Connacht men (except his childhood friend, Ferdia).

That's why he made it his business to kill as many as possible.

So his Uncle Cet swore, "Well then, to even things up I'll have to kill as many Ulstermen as possible!" And so he did.

Twice as Brainy

Cet also prided himself on stealing heads from the head-branch at Eamhain Macha. One day he took the petrified brain of Mesgegra, King of Leinster. "It's like a rock but even harder! I'll use it in my catapult."

Some time later he spotted King Conor and, taking his sling, he fired the brain and saw it lodge in Conor's forehead.

"Now you have two brains," he laughed, "though I don't think you'll be twice as brainy!"

(Conall eventually caught up on his Uncle Cet and killed him in single combat but was so badly wounded himself that he died a short time later.)

Of course Conor wasn't twice as brainy with two brains. He just had a lot of headaches.

"That brain can't be removed without killing you," the doctors told him. "But you'll be all right if you don't get excited!"

"All right? I'm not all right – my head is splitting! And I'm exceedingly ugly! Can you do nothing?"

"Well, we can tell you not to look at yourself and to stay calm."

For a long time Conor followed their advice. But one day, years later, it is said he learned of the death of Christ and got so angry Mesgegra's brain popped from his forehead and instantly he was dead.

The Sons of Usna

But long before that happened Conor had achieved his ambition of forming a great army. And three of his warriors who became famous in legend were Naoise, Ardal and Ainnle, the sons of Usna. They were champion fighters and fought hard for their king.

Then Naoise fell in love with Deirdre who was young and beautiful and loved him too. But the ageing Conor wanted her for his wife. Tragedy followed when she eloped with Naoise to Scotland. Ardal and Ainnle went with them but none of them could escape Conor's revenge.

The King tricked Fergus Mac Roich into bringing them all home, giving Fergus his word they would be safe. Once back in Ulster, Conor's army attacked them and, greatly outnumbered, the brothers died fighting.

Conor married Deirdre but in less than a year she was dead with grief.

Fergus and Maeve

Fergus was furious. "I will no longer serve a king who is so false!" he declared.

The great warrior went to Connacht where he fell in love with Queen Maeve and she with him. Unfortunately Maeve was married to Ailill, who wasn't a bit pleased at this turn of events.

"One day I'll kill Fergus!" Ailill vowed. "But Maeve is a ferocious woman and I don't want to anger her, so I have to be cunning."

The Queen was very beautiful and when she set her mind on something she usually got it. She set her mind on the Brown Bull of Cooley, a mighty animal belonging to Ulster, but he wasn't for sale.

So Maeve declared war and Fergus marched into Ulster by her side.

Defending Ulster

Cúchulainn was defending the ford into the province on his own, for all his comrades were under a sleeping spell. The enemy could advance only singly and Cúchulainn, in one to one combat, stood against them for days on end, killing all he fought.

When Fergus reached the ford and saw only his foster son, whom he loved, he didn't want to fight. Eventually he retreated with his forces.

But Ferdia too was with the Connacht army. He also didn't want to fight his old friend. Then Maeve called him a coward and goaded him into combat.

First the friends fought with equal weapons.
Ferdia's armoured skin kept him safe. He was
a great warrior and after a long hard contest
managed to wound Cúchulainn.

"This is no fair fight!" Cúchulainn was furious and, taking the Gae Bolg, launched it with mighty speed at his best friend. The effect was terrible. The spear-head drove into Ferdia's chest, opened into barbs, and he sank to his knees in agony.

Badly hurt himself, Cúchulainn went to his friend immediately. "We should never have fought," he mourned. "We were the best of comrades. Now we've each caused the other's death."

Ferdia died in great pain and Cúchulainn, much weakened and fearing for Ulster, tied himself upright to a tree, his weapons ready.

Cúchulainn's Death

None of the enemy approached, for they knew how Ferdia had died and were afraid. Cúchulainn's eyes closed and his head dropped. Still they waited. A raven settled on the warrior's shoulder and so they knew for sure he was dead. Only then did they advance.

But by now the Red Branch Knights had woken from the spell. They defeated Maeve's army, but not before she had captured the Brown Bull and brought it back to Connacht.

Fergus Mac Roich returned with Maeve to Connacht. The Queen's husband, Ailill, was fiercely jealous and one day tracked them into the forest. Hearing their laughter and mad with rage, he got a blind archer to fire at Fergus, pretending it was a deer he wanted killed. Fergus had no chance.

Aftermath

For some years after Conor's reign his army continued to exist. But the greatest were dead. Then the training camp closed and, in time, the warriors disbanded.

The Knights lived nearly two thousand years ago yet their deeds have passed into legends that are still told and Cúchulainn, brave and fearless, is a national hero.

He inspired many and his statue stands in the GPO in Dublin, a reminder of his short life and heroic death, as well as being a symbol of the 1916 Easter Rising.

The End

Word Sounds

(Opinions may differ regarding pronunciation)

Words	Sounds
Roich	Ro-ick
Setanta	Set-ant-a
Cernach	Ker-nock
Ferdia	Fer-dee-ah
Cuchullainn	Coo-cull-an
Scathach	Sca-hock
Cet	Ket
Eamhain	Ow-an ('ow' rhymes with 'how')
Macha	Mocka
Mesgegra	Mess-geg-rah
Usna	Us-nah
Naoise	Neesha
Ailill	Al-ill

The Adventures of the Fianna

A Band of Warriors

Long, long ago, when Conn of the Hundred Battles was High King of Ireland, a group of young men was becoming famous. They roamed the land and were known as the Fianna – or Band of Warriors.

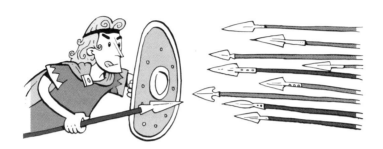

To join the band, a youth had to prove he could run like the wind, race silently through an autumn forest, endure pain without stopping, jump over high branches and defend himself against the spears of nine warriors. Besides all that, he had to know by heart the twelve books of Bardic Poetry.

The Fate of Cumhall

The Fianna's leader was Cumhall, and he was
the bravest and the best of warriors. But one
man held a grudge against him because his
daughter, Muirne, had fallen in love with him
and they had eloped.

"It's not right!" the angry father told the High King. "I gave no permission for her to marry. He has stolen her from me and must be punished!"

So Cumhall was outlawed by the High King.

Anyone could declare war on an outlaw and one of the Fianna, Aedh Mac Mórna, saw his chance to take over as leader. He challenged Cumhall to battle and killed him, but not without losing the sight of one eye. From then on he was known as Goll Mac Mórna, for 'goll' in Irish means blind.

Cumhall left a son and daughter. Muirne never let them forget their father and was always telling stories of his daring deeds as leader of the Fianna. One day, his son Fionn thought, I will be their leader!

Fionn's Boyhood

In childhood he was trained by the wise man, Finnegas, to be a great warrior. And he himself became the wisest person in the world when he was cooking the Salmon of Knowledge for his master. The first to taste the fish would know everything, so Fionn was warned not to taste it. But he burned his thumb on the hot skin and immediately put it in his mouth, and so by accident tasted it first.

By now Conn had died and the High King was Cormac Mac Airt. He heard of the Fianna's great deeds and was very impressed.

I've so many enemies, he thought. I and my palace at Tara could do with some protection!

So Goll and the Fianna agreed to fight for Cormac and protect Tara from Samhain to Bealtaine (Hallowe'en to spring) in return for gold. They were free to hunt during summer and early autumn.

But they didn't do a great job. Every Samhain a particularly nasty fire-breathing dragon sent the warriors to sleep and burned down the palace.

After a couple of years Cormac got fed up. "Why am I paying you?" he asked the warriors. "All you do is snore away while Tara burns! I'm sick of rebuilding it."

Fionn heard the story and said to himself:
Time for me to make my mark.

And so he travelled to Tara and when the monster cast a spell over the warriors and they all nodded off, he stayed awake by prodding his forehead with his spear whenever his eyes started closing. With the same spear he killed the dragon and when the Fianna woke they were overjoyed. He was accepted as their leader, even by Goll Mac Mórna, and even though he was still a boy.

Conan The Bald

The Fianna had many heroes and one of these was Conan Maol (Baldy) Mac Mórna – a brother of Goll. Conan looked nothing like a fighter, being short and wide and totally bald.

He was also inclined to be very rude.

"You're so ugly!" he would say to a plain woman.

"No, I'm not! That's not me!" she would shout indignantly. "That's you looking at your reflection!"

Then there'd be an argument about which of them was the ugliest. It was an argument Conan always won.

In battle his enemies tended to make mistakes about him. "Look at him!" they'd say. "Sure he's so short and enormous he can hardly move. I nearly feel sorry for him."

But it was his enemies who ended up dead. Conan Maol was so brave even the Sidhe – people from the Otherworld with magic power – loved to see him fight. In one battle he had all the skin stripped from his back and was in great pain, but the Sidhe took pity on him and put a sheep's skin against him, where it quickly became part of his own body.

From then on he had a very woolly back,
which did nothing for his looks. Most likely
he had to get sheared every so often. Now and
again a foolish enemy BAAAAAAED at him
and did not live to BAAAAAA again!

(If he'd done much jumping they'd have
called him a Woolly Jumper, but luckily for
his enemies he was too busy fighting to jump
very often.)

The Fastest Man in Ireland

Caoilte Mac Rónáin was another hero. He was the fastest runner in Ireland, possibly the fastest runner on the face of the earth. Once, to win a bet, he ran from Dingle in Kerry to Tara in Meath in less than a day. He was also a great storyteller and those listening around the campfire were spellbound.

But his greatest gift was that he could communicate with animals and make them do his bidding.

One time, Fionn had a row with the High King who threw him into a dungeon at Tara. Fionn didn't try to escape.

If I break out, he thought, Cormac will always be my enemy and will no longer pay the Fianna. I must think of a way to win back his friendship.

While Fionn was thinking, Caoilte came to Tara looking to free his leader.

"I'll release him with no bad feeling on one condition," the High King told him. "You must bring back alive two of every kind of wild animal and bird that lives in Ireland."

Caoilte roamed the land and returned with ducks, geese, swans, ravens, eagles and every other type of bird. Along with these he brought wild horses, foxes, boars, rabbits, hares and all kinds, possibly even a couple of snakes (for this was before Saint Patrick). The din they made approaching Tara was horrible.

Most of the animals didn't want to be in Tara. They wanted to be back home and protested loudly all the way up the hill to the palace, giving out to Caoilte in their own language about the inconvenience. But because they liked him they went with him.

Cormac Mac Airt couldn't stand the racket. All the quacking and howling and shrieking and whinnying gave him a terrible headache. And everyone in the palace was shouting at him, trying to be heard above the noise, wanting an explanation.

Instead he ran in a most unkingly way to where Fionn was imprisoned, grabbed him by the arm and rushed him out the door of Tara.

"Here he is!" he roared at Caoilte. "Get rid of that brigade of lunatics!"

The animals, sensing an insult, took umbrage and created even more of a row.

Fionn told the High King, "He'll send them home if I have a promise that nothing changes between us."

By now the High King was a wreck and would have promised anything. "Yes, yes," he said. "Just make them go away."

So Caoilte spoke a few words and the animals flew, galloped, loped, slithered, rushed and trundled off to their various homes and things went back to normal between the High King and Fionn.

The Battle of Gabhra

Cormac ruled for forty years, paying protection money to the Fianna. Then one day, when he was having his dinner, he choked on a salmon bone and died.

His son, Cairbre, was the next High King and, when he saw the palace accounts, he decided at once that the Fianna were getting no more payment from him.

I don't need their protection, he thought. Fionn is too greedy and has many enemies. I'll raise my own army and fight the Fianna if necessary!

Of course it was necessary, for Fionn felt
he'd given good service for many years, risking
his own and his men's lives.

"We will not be thrown aside by Cairbre!" he told the Fianna. "I'll give him one last chance and send my servant to Tara to collect the gold still owing to us!"

Instead of paying up, Cairbre killed the servant, and so the great Battle of Gabhra began.

Some say Fionn fought alongside his son Oisín and grandson Oscar. The fighting was fierce and Oscar managed to kill Cairbre but died of his own wounds some time later.

Fionn was an old man at this stage, yet fought bravely, killing many. But then he found himself surrounded by five of the enemy, cut off from his friends. Attacked from all sides, he put up a great fight but in the end was slain.

Only twenty warriors altogether survived the battle. Some say Oisín was one and lived on into old age, when he met Saint Patrick and told him all about the Fianna. Others say Oisín never fought at Gabhra, for he was in Tír na nÓg and only met Patrick on his return, centuries later.

The End of the Fianna

What is true is that the Battle of Gabhra broke
the Fianna forever. The glory days were over.
Yet sometimes on the Hill of Tara when
darkness descends and the air is still, it is
said you can hear the voices of the Fianna
and see their shadows around a ghostly fire.

And, if you listen carefully, everything will go quiet as Caoilte Mac Rónáin tells one of his spellbinding stories.

The End

Word Sounds

(Opinions may differ regarding pronunciation)

Words	Sounds
Cumhall	Cool
Muirne	Mwir-neh
Aedh	Ey (to rhyme with Hey)
Goll	Gowl
Fionn	Fee-un
Finnegas	Fin-eh-gas
Samhain	Sow-in (Sow rhymes with How)
Bealtaine	Be-owl-tin-eh
Maol	Mwale
Sidhe	She
Caoilte	Keel-cheh
Cairbre	Car-breh
Gabhra	Gow-rah
Oisin	Usheen